DOLL EMMA

Can you number the pictures to show what
happened first, second, and so on?

Illustrated by Susanne DeMarco

Answer on page 47.

There are many things we sometimes take for granted, including the chance to do a good puzzle. Let us now take a moment to review some things about our nation. 44 words about government can fit into the diagram shown here. Use the number of letters in each word, as well as letter connections, as clues to where it will fit.

MY COUNTRY 'TIS OF THEE

3 Letters	4 Letters	5 Letters	6 Letters	7 Letters
Law	Home	Bills	People	Bravery
	Life	Peace	Pledge	Citizen
	Veto	Power	Rights	Courage
	Vote	Pride	Senate	Freedom
		Stars	Speech	Honesty
		Taxes	Treaty	Justice
		Union		Liberty
				Stripes

8 Letters	9 Letters	10 Letters	11 Letters	12 Letters
Assembly	Democracy	Allegiance	Legislative	Independence
Congress	Executive	Government	Responsible	
Democrat	Happiness	Republican		
Election	Necessity			
Judicial	President			
Politics	Standards			

Illustrated by Tom Powers

FIND FOUR

These four toy boxes are all different, but if you look carefully,
you should be able to find four objects that appear in each one.

Illustrated by Gregg Valley

Answer on page 47.

DOT MAGIC

Join these dots to find a nice place to visit.

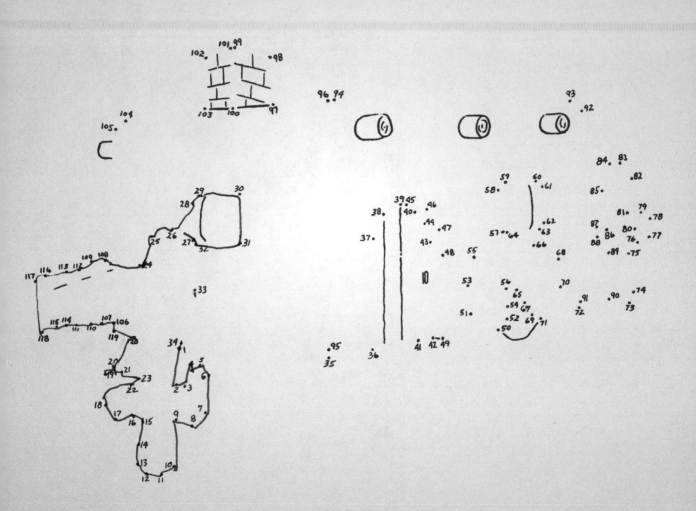

Answer on page 47.

GLOBE PROBE

That intrepid explorer, Dr. Cincinnati Holmes, is trying to figure out the itinerary for his next trip. Can you use his map to help answer each question below to send him on his way? You may want to check an encyclopedia or atlas for exact distances. If you find all the correct answers, place the first letter of each choice in the blanks on page 9 to discover where Cincinnati wants to end up.

1. Is it farther from Germany to Sweden or to France?

_____

2. Is it farther from Angola to Ethiopia or to Russia?

_____

3. Is it farther from Morocco to Iraq or to Iran?

_____

4. Is it farther from Panama to Mexico or to Libya?

_____

5. Is it farther from China to Australia or to Thailand?

_____

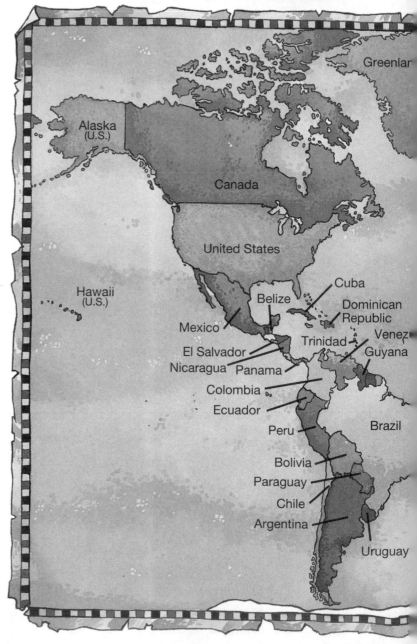

Illustrated by John Nez

6. Is it farther from Algeria to Namibia or to Sudan?

_____

7. Is it farther from Ghana to Kenya or to Nigeria?

_____

8. Is it farther from Panama to Colombia or to Argentina?

_____

Cincinnati's destination:

___ ___ ___ ___ ___ ___ ___ ___
 1   2   3   4   5   6   7   8

Finland
Sweden
Iceland
Norway
Denmark
Germany
Russia
England
France
Ireland
Hungary
Bulgaria
Italy
Kazakhstan
Spain
Mongolia
Afghanistan
Portugal
Turkey
China
Japan
Morocco
Iran
Pakistan
Mali
Algeria Libya
Myanmar
N. Korea
Laos
S. Korea
India
Taiwan
Iraq
Vietnam
Sudan
Qatar
Philippines
Israel
Egypt
Sierra
Leone
Ethiopia
Sri Lanka
Indonesia
Benin
Ghana
Kenya
Thailand
Nigeria
Chad
Congo
Tanzania
Angola
Madagascar
Namibia
Australia
New Zealand
Botswana
Mozambique
Zimbabwe
Zambia
South Africa

Antarctica

GOING UP

Can you match each person with the floor they want?

 Answer on page 47.

LAUNDRY MEMORIES

Part I

OPEN 9 TO 9

Take a long look at this picture. Try to remember everything you see in it. Then turn the page and try to answer some questions about it without looking back.

Illustrated by Anni Matsick

DON'T READ THIS UNTIL YOU HAVE LOOKED AT "Laundry Memories—Part I" ON PAGE 11.

LAUNDRY MEMORIES Part II

Can you answer these questions about the laundry scene you saw? Don't peek!

1. Was anyone wearing a hat?
2. How many dryers were seen?
3. What hours was this laundromat open?
4. How many tops of washing machines were up?
5. What brand of soap powder could be seen, besides FOAMY?
6. Were there any clothes on hangers?
7. Was the sink water on or off?
8. What color laundry bag was the boy carrying?
9. Was he carrying liquid or powder soap?
10. What loose item of clothing was on the floor?

Answer on page 47.

THE KINDEST CUT

Big Antny wants to get the most slices out of a single pizza.
Athena says she can get 11 slices of unequal size in only four cuts.
Assist Antny to ascertain the actuality of this assessment.

Answer on page 48.

Illustrated by Terry Kovalcik

FLOAT YOUR BOAT

Sail from the mainland to the island by navigating from water vessel to water vessel. If you bump into a land vessel, you'll sink and have to start over.

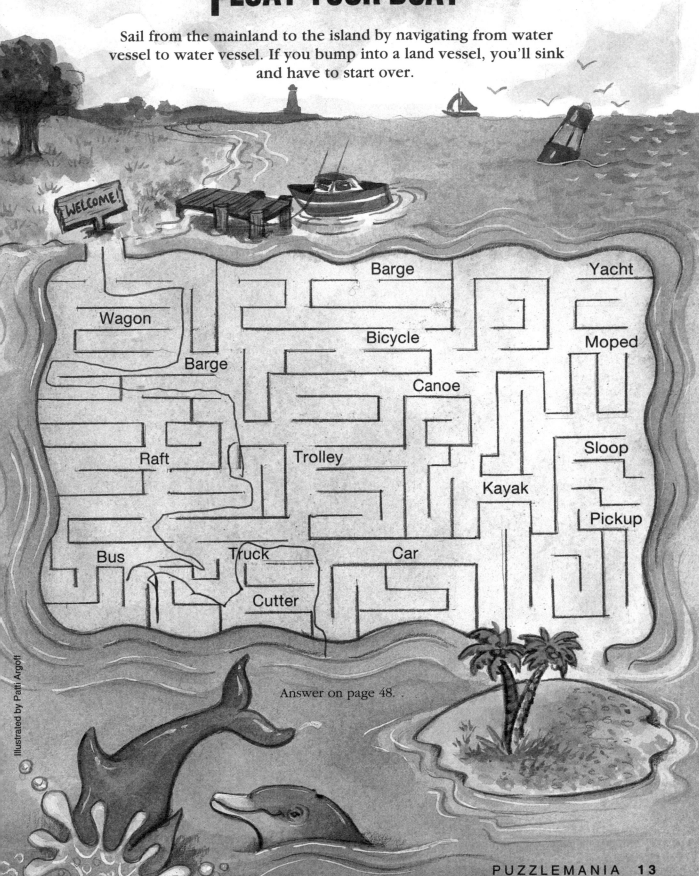

Answer on page 48.

Illustrated by Patti Argoff

CHECKMATE!

Keep a sharp eye on your opponent as you try to solve these clues. Each answer can be made from the letters in CHECKMATE.

ACROSS
1. Tennis contest
5. Postal abbreviation for Connecticut
7. Past tense of 9 across
8. Dull pain
9. Have a meal or snack
11. First two vowels in reverse order
12. Wizard of Oz aunt
14. Scottish cap
15. Every individual one
18. Sandwich meat
19. Interjection or cough
22. Abbreviation for extra-terrestrial
23. Trap or hook
25. Purr-fect pet
26. Third person pronoun

DOWN
1. Prepare, build, or cook
2. Preposition for place
3. Golf ball holder
4. Sombrero
5. Violate the rules
6. Group of players
10. Abbreviation for the American Kennel Club
13. Ham, lamb, or Spam
16. Initials for the morning
17. Miami's basketball team
18. Dress border
20. Abbreviation for height
21. Article
23. Postal abbreviation for California
24. Chess abbreviation for "check"

Illustrated by Mark Corcoran

Answer on page 48.

HALFWAY TO THE STARS

How many differences can you spot between these two scenes?

Illustrated by Frank Bolle

A SONG OF SIXPENCE

The King is in his counting house, counting out his money. But can you help the royal exchequer be sure the royal budget comes out correctly by double-checking the King's numbers? Use the conversion chart to find the value of each coin.

COINS	DOLLARS
Gold	1.00
Silver	.50
Brass	.25
Tin	.10

	Gold	Silver	Brass	Tin	Total
Monday					
Tuesday					
Thursday					

On Monday, the King counted 43 gold, 41 silver, 60 brass, and 16 tin coins. What was the total value?

On Tuesday, the King counted 25 gold, 63 silver, 30 brass, and 29 tin coins. What was the total value?

On Wednesday, the King went fishing.

On Thursday, the King counted 56 gold, 32 silver, 27 brass, and 41 tin coins. What was the total value?

On which day did the King count the most coins?

On which day did his coins have the highest value?

On which day did the King have the most fun?

Answer on page 48.

Illustrated by Charles Jordan

PICTURE MIXER

Copy these mixed-up squares in the spaces on the next page to put this picture back together. The letters and numbers tell you where each square belongs. The first one, A-3, has been done for you.

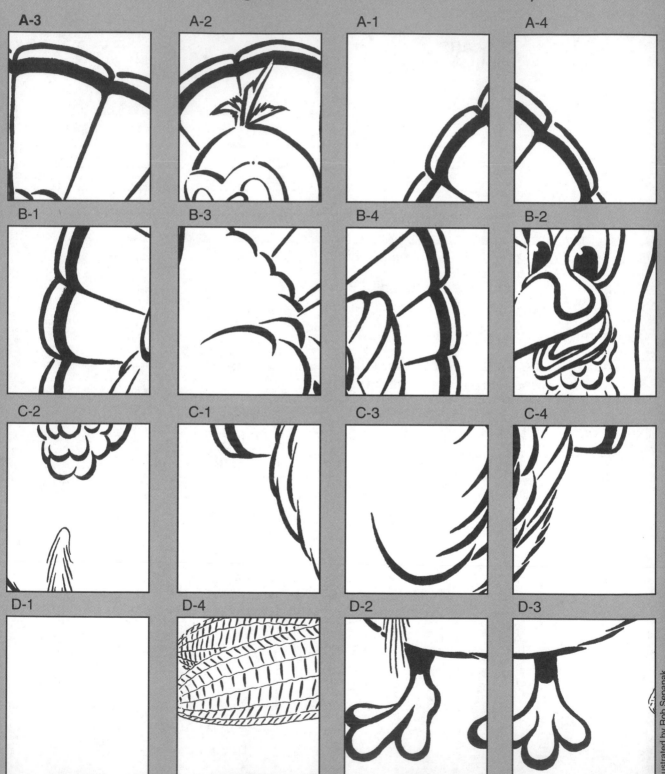

A-3 A-2 A-1 A-4

B-1 B-3 B-4 B-2

C-2 C-1 C-3 C-4

D-1 D-4 D-2 D-3

Illustrated by Rob Sepanak

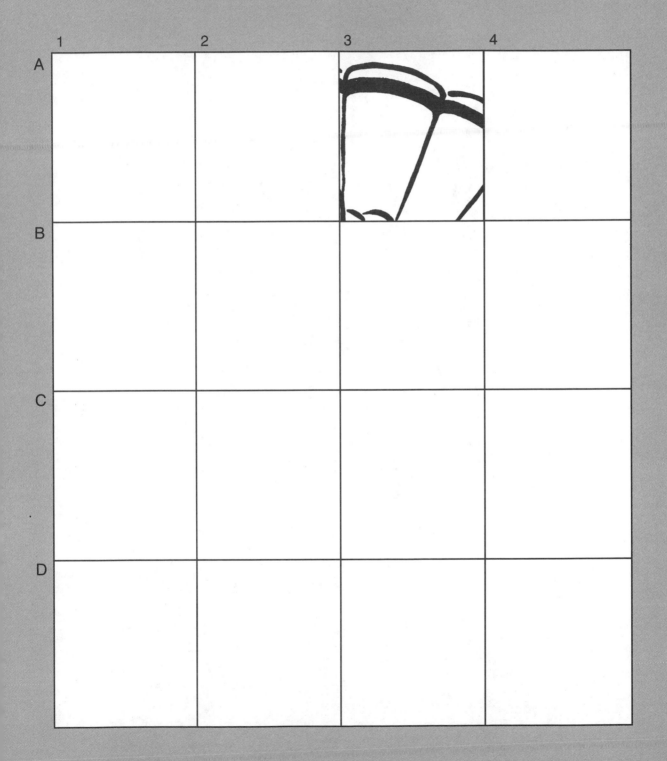

BEE POSITIVE

You should be able to
help this buzzer find
three matching pairs of
flowers in this garden.

HHHHHHHHHMMMMMMMMMMMMMMMMMMMMMMMMM

Answer on page 48.

STOP, LOOK, AND LIST

Under each category, list one thing that begins with each letter. For example, one method of transportation that begins with A is Airplane. See if you can name another.

METHODS OF TRANSPORTATION

A ______________________________

B ______________________________

C ______________________________

F ______________________________

S ______________________________

INSECTS

A ______________________________

B ______________________________

C ______________________________

F ______________________________

S ______________________________

POST OFFICE WORDS

A ______________________________

B ______________________________

C ______________________________

F ______________________________

S ______________________________

Illustrated by Lisa Dayer

Answer on page 48.

CELL DIVISION

By Saturday night, the Tombstone town jail was full, with one desperado in each of the jail's six cells. Use the clues from Sheriff Goodguy's report to figure out who committed what crime (including public loudness), what day they were brought in, and in which cell the Sheriff put each outlaw.

1. Monday - Put the card cheat in cell five this morning. In afternoon, had to arrest Slippery Lou.

2. Tuesday - Arrested litterbug.

3. Wednesday - Locked Horrible Harry in the cell directly across from Terrible Tim, and next to Mean Mike, both of whom were already in. Mike has the odd-numbered cell closest to the door.

4. Thursday - Caught a cattle rustler. Put him in cell four until the judge could see him.

5. Friday - Wicked Will was peddling without a license. He was peddling some new-fangled contraption called a bicycle. Thing will never catch on. Had to bring Will in.

Illustrated by Anthony Accardo

Answer on page 49.

Day	Name	Crime	Cell

6. Sneaky Sam was glad Wicked Will was put in a facing cell, because then they could swap jokes.

7. The one who was speeding on his horse complained about not getting one of the cells closest to the door.

ROW, ROW, ROW

Every map section here has something in common with the two other sections in the same row. For example, each section in the top three folds across features some houses. Look at the other map sections across, down, and diagonally. Can you tell what's the same in each row of three?

Illustrated by Barbara Gray

Answer on page 49.

AM I BLUE?

Can you unscramble the words below to find a list of things that go along with or follow the word BLUE?

kin
yaj
sargs
pichs
rebries
sajen
trawe
tila lyf
arlcol
hawle
ronbib
kartes
nirpt
hesece
drib
vanehe
tonben
derab

Illustrated by Paul Richer

Answer on page 49.

HIDDEN PICTURES

There are at least 18 objects hidden in this picture.
How many can you find?

STATE U.

Illustrated by Maurie Jo Manning

CIRCULAR THINKING

Put the letters of these nine circles in order from the simplest drawing to the most complex. A message should appear if you figure this one out.

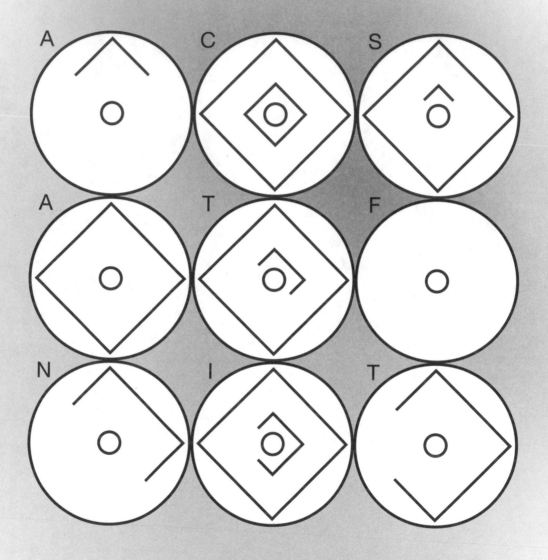

Answer on page 49.

AVE AND AVE NOT

Can you help Maria figure out which letters to add to the clues to find the words that contain the letters AVE?

Keep or rescue: __ AVE

Donated: __ AVE

Possess: __ AVE

Bear's home: __ AVE

Surge of water: __ AVE

Part of a roof that overhangs: __ AVE

Cut off whiskers: __ __ AVE

No-good scoundrel: __ __ AVE

Courage: __ __ AVE __ __

Come apart, in loose strings: __ __ __ AVE __

Sidewalk and street: __ AVE __ __ __ __

Spooky place at Halloween: __ __ AVE __ __ __ __

Illustrated by Randy Verougstraete

Answer on page 49.

BY THE NUMBERS

You'll score big points if you identify the object on
which these numbers are found.

Illustrated by Michelle Gugliotta

Answer on page 49.

TOSSING THE HORSEHIDE

The horsehide is one nickname for a baseball. This puzzle contains the nicknames of 18 famous baseball players. The names are hidden across, up, down, backward, and diagonally. Once you've found all the names and put the players into rotation, read the uncircled letters from left to right, top to bottom, to discover what helps win this game. We've placed a man on first to get you started.

Babe
Boog
Catfish
Dizzy
Duke
Hank

Lefty
Nellie
Pee Wee
Rusty
Sandy
Satchell

Smokey
Sparky
Tony
~~Ty~~
~~Yaz~~
Yogi

Leftover letters:

_ _ _ _ _ _ _ _ _   _ _ _ _ _

Answer on page 49.

```
H S A T C H E L L
O M M Z A Y R E E
H R S O E K U D F
S P A R K Y S N T
I E N K T E T E Y
F E D N B U Y L Z
T W Y A O N N L Z
A E B H O S O I I
C E Y O G I T E D
```

LIST LINKS

Can you crack the code for each list here? Once you've deciphered each list, see if you can tell what common bond is shared by all the items in that list. The code is the same for all the lists.

A=1	G=7	M=13	S=19	Y=25
B=2	H=8	N=14	T=20	Z=26
C=3	I=9	O=15	U=21	
D=4	J=10	P=16	V=22	
E=5	K=11	Q=17	W=23	
F=6	L=12	R=18	X=24	

1. 12-9-12-25

   18-15-19-5

   9-18-9-19

   4-1-9-19-25

   22-9-15-12-5-20

2. 7-14-21

   2-5-1-18

   2-5-5

   1-14-20

   2-15-1-18

3. 5-22-5

   14-1-14

   2-15-2

   15-20-20-15

   8-1-14-14-1-8

4. 16-9-7-19-11-9-14

   3-1-20-20-1-9-12

   4-15-7-23-15-15-4

   3-18-1-2-1-16-16-12-5

   8-15-18-19-5-18-1-4-9-19-8

Answer on page 50.

Illustrated by Sherry Neidigh

32

X-CELLENT

Uh oh, Bubba's back in the hospital. You can assist by filling in the X-ray to show the doctor what is giving Bubba a bellyache.

Illustrated by
Marc Nadel

FUN HOUSE

Be careful, there's a lot of activity in this activity. To help the workmen solve the riddle below, read each clue and then write the appropriate letter above the space with the correct number.

Letter one is near the bricks for the chimney.
Look in the mailbox for the fourth letter.
The front door is showing letter nine.
The sixth letter is on the side of a toolbox.
Letter number eight is in the bathtub on the second floor.
Check the wheelbarrow for letter twelve.
Letter two is hanging in the living room.
The tenth letter is in the rosebush.
Rufus is chewing on letter five.
Look on the roof tiles for letter three.
The shutters show letter eleven.
Letter seven is hanging on the rafters.

Why did the farmer put up corncob wallpaper?

___ ___   ___ ___ ___   ___ ___ ___ ___ ___
 1   2   3   4   5   6   7   8   8   1

___ ___ ___ ___ ___   ___ ___ ___ ___   ___ ___ ___ ___ .
 6   2   9   8 10   4   7 11   5   5   7 12   1

Answer on page 50.

Illustrated by R. Michael Palan

3 4

MULTIPLE SHAPES

Find each shape shown below inside the big square. Then multiply the numbers inside each shape. Put the letter for each shape on the space above the correct answer to the multiplication. If you get the right answers, you'll solve a funny riddle.

What's black and yellow and goes "Zzub, zzub?"

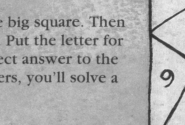

Illustrated by T. F. Cook

Answer on page 50.

$$\overline{\underset{63}{A}} \quad \overline{24} \quad \overline{30} \quad \overline{72} \quad \overline{48} \quad \overline{21} \quad \overline{32} \quad \overline{12} \quad \overline{54} \quad \overline{42}$$

$$\overline{40} \quad \overline{28} \quad \overline{45} \quad \overline{35} \quad \overline{20} \quad \overline{40} \quad \overline{56} \quad \overline{80} \quad \overline{49}$$

WHAT'S IN A WORD?

Our marvelous magician has conjured up a list of words made from the letters in the word MARVELOUS. All his words are at least three letters long, and there are no plurals that end in "s". He conjured up at least 55 words, including words like SAVE and VASE. How many can you pull out of your hat?

Answer on page 50.

Illustrated by Tim Ellis

JIGSAW

Can you tell which pieces below belong in the empty spaces?

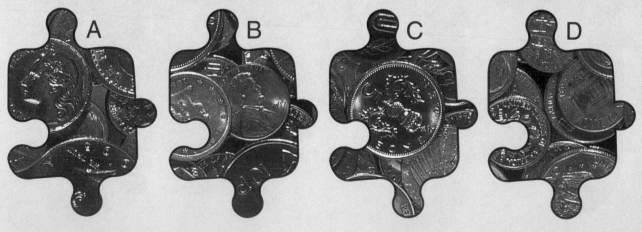

Photo by Jerard Solinger

Answer on page 50.

SECOND VERSE, DIFFERENT FROM THE FIRST

The choir is cranky because their music got mixed up. You can help straighten the songs by coming up with the line that comes just before each line shown below. It might help you remember the missing lines if you sing each well-known song.

...How I wonder what you are. **1**

...Gently down the stream. **2**

...For amber waves of grain. **3**

...Bake me a cake as fast as you can. **4**

...And Bingo was its name-o. **5**

...To Grandmother's house we go. **6**

...And the deer and the antelope play. **7**

...His name is my name, too. **8**

...Stuck a feather in his cap and called it macaroni. **9**

...Four and twenty blackbirds baked in a pie. **10**

Illustrated by Jerry Zimmerman

Answer on page 50.

THINK OF THAT

Each scientist listed here invented or discovered something important. To discover the answers, scan the code number before each name. Then go through the grid and write down each letter that has the same number. For example, for Michael Faraday, find all the letters with the number one over them. Copy the letters in order and you'll soon be a genius, too.

1. Michael Faraday (1791-1867) discovered benzene, which is used in making detergents and nylons. He also developed this.

2. Thomas Alva Edison (1847-1931) had more than 1,000 patents in his own name. One of his inventions was the electric light bulb. He also invented this.

3. Benjamin Franklin (1706-1790) was a United States diplomat, a scientist, and an author. He was also one of the signers of the Declaration of Independence. Name one of his inventions.

4. Marie Curie (1867-1934) won the Nobel Peace Prize for Chemistry in 1911 for discovering this new element. What is it?

5. Sir Isaac Newton (1642-1727) discovered the law of gravity and invented the math method called calculus. What else did he invent?

6. Bartolomeo Cristofori (1655-1731) was an Italian harpsichord maker. He invented an early version of this instrument.

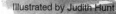
Illustrated by Judith Hunt

7. James Naismith (1861-1939) invented this game using two peach baskets and a soccer ball.

3	1	2	5	7	6	7	3	4	1	5	7	2	5	7	1	3	7	2	7	1	2	6	3	4	5	1	3
L	E	M	R	B	P	A	I	R	L	E	S	O	F	K	E	G	E	T	T	C	I	I	H	A	L	T	T

5	7	6	7	1	2	7	3	5	1	7	1	5	2	2	3	5	1	4	2	5	6	1	3	2	5	2	1
E	B	A	A	R	O	L	N	C	I	L	C	T	N	P	I	I	M	D	I	N	N	O	N	C	G	T	T

3	2	4	5	2	1	2	5	3	6	2	4	5	1	2	5	2	3	5	2	5	4	5	2	3	5	2	5
G	U	I	T	R	O	E	E	R	O	C	U	L	R	A	E	M	O	S	E	C	M	O	R	D	P	A	E

1. _____ _____

2. _____ _____ _____

3. _____ _____

4. _____

5. _____ _____

6. _____   7. _____

Answer on page 50.

41

REINDEER GAMES

Can you help Herbie find which reindeer are tied to each lead?

Answer on page 50.

INSTANT PICTURE

Don't be afraid to fill in each section that contains two dots.

Illustrated by Rob Sepanak

Answer on page 50.

CAT & DOG MYSTERY

Case # 240
Close Encounters

Clue Cat and Deductive Dog were at the Petropolis Police Station working on something very important. They had a crossword puzzle spread out on Dog's desk. They were stuck for a ten-letter word where "dog" and "cat" appear next to one another. They both looked up as Tab Lloyd came into the room.

Tab was the editor for the Petropolis Daily Peanut newspaper. As a kitten, he and Clue Cat had been friends on the streets. They had stayed in touch over the years and often did favors for one another. Cat would occasionally help Tab out with a tough question, and Tab would help the police by making sure the right story got into the paper.

"What can we do for you, Tab?" Dog asked.

Tab held up a photograph.

"Can you take a look at this?" he asked. "Diane Foxsey is an explorer who claims she just got back from Alaska. She says she took this picture on her trip and wants to sell it to the paper for $1,000. I'd like to buy it, but I need to make sure it isn't a fake."

Both Cat and Dog looked the photo over carefully. To their amazement, it showed what looked like a gleaming spaceship about to land among some trees. On the side of the flying saucer were strange, black markings that looked like some sort of code. The entire rim of the saucer was surrounded with wild colored lights.

"Diane thinks the markings may be some kind of alien language," Tab informed them. "The only trouble is, you can't make out enough of them to tell."

"Where did she say she took the picture?" Deductive Dog asked.

"In an unexplored region of Alaskan tundra," Tab answered. "Her entire trip makes for a great story. That's why I'm interested in buying the photograph.

"Diane claims that she and the members of her expedition were the only civilized things for three hundred miles in any direction. They walked for six weeks across the northern tundra wasteland, trying to reach the North Pole. At night they slept in a house made of snow."

"Igloo," Cat said.

"That was the answer to fourteen across," Dog pointed out. "What you'd use to fix a broken Ig."

Cat nodded and wrote it down.

Tab wasn't sure what they were talking about but was too polite to ask.

"Anyway," he said, "I need to know what you think. Is this photo real or a hoax?"

"If I were you, I'd save my $1,000 for a more honest photographer." Dog tossed the picture back on the desk.

"They say a picture is worth a thousand words," Clue Cat snickered. "But this one isn't worth even a single dollar."

WHY DO THE DETECTIVES THINK THE PHOTO OF THE UFO WAS FAKED?

Once you solve this case, see how many aliens and U.F.O.S are hidden in the picture.

Bonus question: Can you think of a ten-letter word where "dog" and "cat" appear next to one another?

Answer on page 50.

BOX SCORES

Follow the arrows from box to box, placing the same letters in each connected box. Some starting letters have already been put in for you, while some other letters need to be guessed. The more letters you fill in, the easier it gets. When you're finished, you should be able to read a funny riddle.

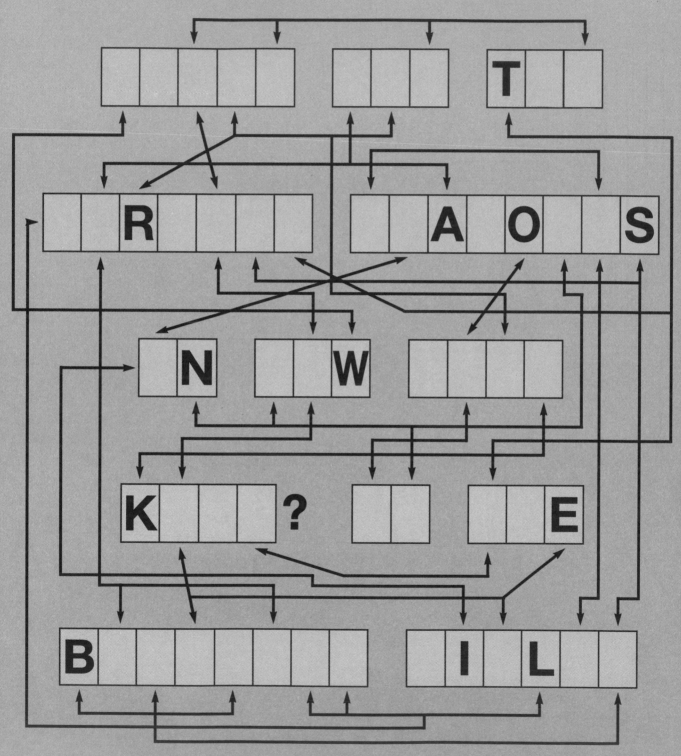

Answer on page 50.

ANSWERS

DOLL EMMA (page 3)

4	3
6	2
1	5

MY COUNTRY 'TIS OF THEE (pages 4-5)

FIND FOUR (page 6)

DOT MAGIC (page 7)

GLOBE PROBE (pages 8-9)

1. Sweden
2. Russia
3. Iran
4. Libya
5. Australia
6. Namibia
7. Kenya
8. Argentina

Cincinnati's destination: SRI LANKA

GOING UP (page 10)

1 - A
2 - B
3 - E
4 - F
5 - C
6 - D

LAUNDRY MEMORIES (page 12)

1. Yes	8. Green
2. Five	9. Liquid
3. 9 to 9	10. One sock
4. Three	
5. Sudso	
6. Yes	
7. Off	

THE KINDEST CUT (page 12)

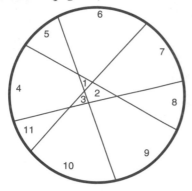

FLOAT YOUR BOAT (page 13)

CHECKMATE! (pages 14-15)

M	A	T	C	H		C	T
A	T	E		A	C	H	E
K		E	A	T		E	A
E	M		K		T	A	M
	E	A	C	H		T	
H	A	M		E	H		T
E	T		C	A	T	C	H
M		C	A	T		H	E

A SONG OF SIXPENCE (page 17)

	Gold	Silver	Brass	Tin	Total
Monday	43.00	20.50	15.00	1.60	80.10
Tuesday	25.00	31.50	7.50	2.90	66.90
Thursday	56.00	16.00	6.75	4.10	82.85

Day with most coins? Monday
Day with highest value? Thursday
Day with most fun? Wednesday

PICTURE MIXER (pages 18-19)

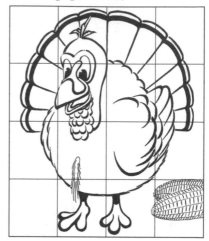

BEE POSITIVE (page 20)

STOP, LOOK, AND LIST (page 21)

Here are our answers. You may have found others.

METHODS OF TRANSPORTATION	INSECTS	POST OFFICE WORDS
Automobile	Ant	Address
Bus	Bee	Box
Canoe	Cricket	Cancel
Ferry	Fly	Freight
Sailboat	Silverfish	Stamp

CELL DIVISION (pages 22-23)

From a quick read, we know that Lou and the card cheat were arrested on Monday. The litterbug was arrested on Tuesday. Harry was arrested on Wednesday and put in with Mike and Tim. Therefore, Mike and Tim must be the card cheat and the litterbug, in some order. We also discover that Mike is in cell one. Since Harry is next to Mike, Harry must be in cell two, and Tim is across the hall in cell five.

On Thursday, the cattle rustler got put into cell four. Wicked Will was peddling and was arrested on Friday. Sam and Will are in facing cells. The only two facing cells left by this time are cell three and cell four. Since we know Will is the peddler, and we know the rustler is in cell four, Sam must be the rustler and Will must be in cell three.

So here's what we know so far:

Monday	Lou		
Monday	Tim	Card Cheat	Five
Tuesday	Mike	Litterbug	One
Wednesday	Harry		Two
Thursday	Sam	Rustler	Four
Friday	Will	Peddler	Three

By the process of elimination, Lou must be in cell six. And since the speeder didn't get cells one or six, Lou must be the person who was too loud. This leaves Harry to be the speeder.

ROW, ROW, ROW (page 24)

river   hills   bridges   measurement

houses

tree

rips

road

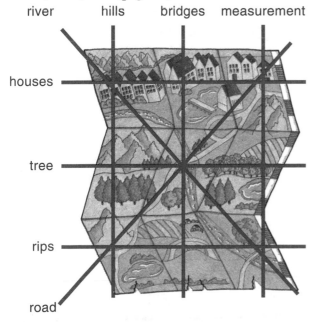

AM I BLUE? (page 25)

ink	whale
jay	ribbon
grass	streak
chips	print
berries	cheese
jeans	bird
water	heaven
tail fly	bonnet
collar	beard

CIRCULAR THINKING (page 28)

FANTASTIC

AVE AND AVE NOT (page 29)

save	shave
gave	knave
have	bravery
cave	unravel
wave	pavement
eave	graveyard

BY THE NUMBERS (page 30)

TV Remote	Computer Keyboard
Radio Dial	Playing Card
Ruler	Telephone Pad
Calculator	Clock

TOSSING THE HORSEHIDE (page 31)

Leftover letters: HOME RUNS

LIST LINKS (page 32)

1. Lily, Rose, Iris, Daisy, Violet.
   Girls' names that are flowers.
2. Gnu, bear, bee, ant, boar.
   Animals that are homophones of other words.
3. Eve, Nan, Bob, Otto, Hannah.
   Names that are palindromes.
4. Pigskin, cattail, dogwood, crabapple, horseradish.
   Compound words that contain animal names.

FUN HOUSE (pages 34-35)

Why did the farmer put up corncob wallpaper?
SO THE WALLS WOULD HAVE EARS.

MULTIPLE SHAPES (page 36)

What is black and yellow and goes, "Zzub, zzub?" A BEE FLYING BACKWARDS

WHAT'S IN A WORD? (page 37)

Here is our list of 71 words. You may have found others.

alms, are, arm, ear, earl, elm, era, lame, laser, lore, lose, louse, love, lover, lure, male, mar, mare, marvel, meal, mole, moral, more, mouse, move, mule, muse, oar, oral, ore, oval, over, ram, rave, real, realm, ream, roam, role, rose, rouse, rove, rue, rule, ruse, sale, salve, same, save, sea, seal, seam, sear, slam, slave, smear, sole, solve, sore, soul, suave, sum, sure, use, vale, valor, value, vase, veal, velour, vole

JIGSAW (page 38)

1 - D, 2 - B, 3 - A, C - Leftover

SECOND VERSE, DIFFERENT FROM THE FIRST (page 39)

1. Twinkle, twinkle, little star...
2. Row, row, row, your boat...
3. O beautiful for spacious skies...
4. Pat-a-cake, pat-a-cake, baker's man...
5. There was a farmer had a dog...
6. Over the river and through the woods...
7. O give me a home where the buffalo roam...
8. John Jacob Jingleheimer Schmidt...
9. Yankee Doodle went to town, riding on a pony...
10. Sing a song of sixpence, pocketful of rye...

THINK OF THAT (pages 40-41)

1. Electric motor
2. Motion picture camera
3. Lightning rod
4. Radium
5. Reflecting telescope
6. Piano
7. Basketball

REINDEER GAMES (page 42)

1 - D/B, 2 - R, 3 - C/C, 4 - D/D, 5 - P/V

INSTANT PICTURE (page 43)

CAT & DOG (pages 44-45)

CASE #240 - CLOSE ENCOUNTERS
Since there are trees in the picture, it could not have been taken on the Alaskan tundra. An area of land is called a tundra only if it is a vast, nearly level, TREELESS region. The detectives felt that if the photographer lied about *where* she took the picture, she probably also lied about *what* was in the picture.

Tab Lloyd was so grateful to the sleuths for saving him $1,000 that he gave them the crossword answer that had them stumped.

Bonus: A ten-letter word where "dog" appears next to "cat" is DOGCATCHER.

BOX SCORES (page 46)

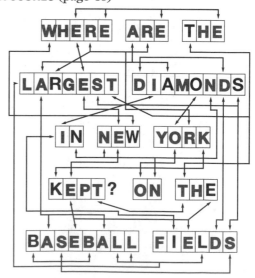